ORFF-SCHULWERK
in the African Tradition

African Songs and Rhythms for Children
A Selection from Ghana

by

William Komla Amoaku

ED 6376

ISMN 979-0-001-06790-4

www.schott-music.com

Mainz · London · Berlin · Madrid · New York · Paris · Prague · Tokyo · Toronto
© 1971 SCHOTT MUSIC GmbH & Co. KG, Mainz · Printed in Germany

VORWORT

Nach afrikanischer Tradition sind Sprache, Rhythmus und Bewegung die Marksteine auf dem Wege zur Musik. Das ORFF-SCHULWERK, das ihnen noch die für alles Musizieren unerläßliche Komponente des Schöpferischen hinzufügt, steht daher der afrikanischen Vorstellung vom Musikmachen sehr nahe. Es ist uns daher eine Freude, dieses erste Heft des ORFF-SCHULWERKS herauszubringen, das unter persönlicher, kompetenter Obhut von Dr. Carl Orff durch Komla Amoaku, einen Musiker aus Ghana, im Geiste der afrikanischen Musiktradition erarbeitet worden ist.

Das Heft fußt ausschließlich auf afrikanischem Material und beginnt daher folgerichtig mit Sprache, Gesang und Schlagwerk, und nicht mit rein instrumentaler Musik. Für jene, die das Orff-Schulwerk hauptsächlich in Verbindung mit Schlagwerkinstrumenten bestimmter Tonhöhe kennen, möchte diese Publikation einen wichtigen Hinweis auf andere Möglichkeiten geben, die das Schulwerk anbietet.

Wir hoffen, daß die hiermit vorgelegte Auswahl nicht nur Musikerzieher in Afrika interessieren wird sondern auch alle Pädagogen, die mit dem ORFF-SCHULWERK nach europäischer Tradition vertraut sind, Ihre Schüler aber auch mit den Musiktraditionen anderer Länder bekanntmachen wollen.

J. J. Kwabena Nketia
Universität Ghana,
Legon.

PREFACE

The traditional African approach to music is through speech, rhythm and movement. ORFF-SCHULWERK which combines these with a creative approach to musicianship, therefore, comes very close to the African concept of music making. It is for this reason that we are happy to launch this first volume of ORFF-SCHULWERK in the African tradition prepared by Komla Amoaku, a Ghanaian musician, under the able guidance of Dr. Carl Orff himself. Based entirely on African materials, the starting point of this little volume is, quite rightly, speech, song and percussion and not pure instrumental music. For those who associate the Orff method first and foremost with tuned percussion, therefore, it should come as a revelation of other possibilities that the method offers.

It is our hope that the selection presented in this book will be of interest not only to music educators in Africa but also to educators accustomed to ORFF-SCHULWERK in the European tradition who wish to expose their pupils to the musical traditions of other lands.

J. H. Kwabena Nketia
University of Ghana,
Legon.

EINFÜHRUNG

Wenn man am Tag irgendwelcher öffentlicher Zeremonien oder zum Erntefest in eine ghanesische Stadt kommt, wird einem sogleich auffallen, daß trommeln, singen und tanzen vor allem anderen Tun und Treiben Vorrang haben. Die Ghanesen haben, wie andere afrikanische Volksstämme auch, viel Freude am Musizieren. Infolgedessen hat jeder den Wunsch, singen und tanzen zu lernen, damit er diese Freude mit anderen teilen kann.

Das verfügbare Repertoire an Stücken, die von Generation zu Generation weitergegeben werden, ist groß, doch wird die musikalische Tradition nicht nur auf diese Weise lebendig erhalten, sondern auch durch die Anregung zu eigenschöpferischer Betätigung und Improvisation während der Darbietung selbst.

DIE LIEDER

Die in diese Auswahl aufgenommenen Lieder stammen aus dem Liedgut der Ghanesen, die sich der Sprachen Akan, Ga und Ewe bedienen. Gleich anderen afrikanischen Völkern haben auch die Ghanesen ihre Kinderlieder, Lieder für die heranwachsende Jugend und Lieder für Erwachsene. Es gibt auch Lieder, die von verschiedenen gesellschaftlichen Gruppen — wie zum Beispiel Religionsgemeinschaften oder Kriegern — gesungen werden. Bei bestimmten Anlässen kommen auch Angehörige solcher verschiedenartiger Gruppen gemeinsam zusammen. Auch Kinder dürfen, obgleich sie sich in der Regel bei ihren eigenen Veranstaltungen produzieren, gelegentlich an manchen Zusammenkünften der Erwachsenen beteiligen — so etwa bei Abenden, an denen Geschichten erzählt werden oder bei anderen geselligen Anlässen. Auf diese Weise lernen sie nicht nur Lieder, die ihrer Altersgruppe zugehören, sondern auch solche, die von ihren Eltern gesungen werden.

Die vorliegende Auswahl umfaßt Wiegenlieder, Gesänge, die dem Kleinen Trost, Mut und Rat bringen sollen, oder von Abenteuern berichten, und wieder andere, die abwesender Freunde gedenken. In Ghana ist es üblich, ein Trankopfer darzubringen, wenn man zu Gott — dem Höchsten Wesen — oder auch zu einer niederen Gottheit betet, oder auch seine Vorfahren anruft. Auch ein solches Trankopferlied findet sich in diesem Heft.

Nicht alle Verse werden gesungen. Manche werden gesprochen, manche auf Instrumenten wiedergegeben — wie zum Beispiel auf *atumpan* — das sind Sprechtrommeln; denn Trommeln können die Sprechstimme ersetzen. (Der Trommler ahmt Tonfall und Rhythmus der Worte auf seinem Instrument nach.) Ein derartiges, auf einen „getrommelten Text" basierendes Versarrangement wurde gleichfalls aufgenommen.

Das Singen in den drei ghanesischen Landessprachen — Twi, Ga und Ewe — wird allen Spaß machen. Zur Erleichterung der Aussprache haben wir eine kleine phonetische Anleitung beigefügt.

SCHLAGWERK

Die Lieder in diesem Heft sind im Rhythmus festgelegt und werden von Schlaginstrumenten begleitet, was dem Sänger hilft, streng im Takt zu bleiben. Die einfachste und somit häufigste Form der Schlagwerkbegleitung ist das Händeklatschen. Ist man daran nicht gewöhnt, kann man beim Singen dieser Lieder eine ausreichende Fertigkeit in dieser Technik erwerben. Beim Klatschen sollte man gelöst sein, die Arme schwingen lassen und sich im ganzen Körper mitwiegen.

Es gibt noch andere Schlaginstrumente, die man zur Verdeutlichung des Grundschlags oder für Begleitrhythmen verwendet. Statt Händeklatschen kann man zwei Stäbe oder Metallkastagnetten gegeneinanderschlagen. Andere beliebte Instrumente sind einzelne oder doppelte Glokken ohne Klöppel, verschiedene Rasseln und der Gong.

Hier einige ghaneische Namen für diese Instrumente:

Instrument	Ewe	Twi
Rassel	akaye, axatse	torowa
Kastagnetten		firikyiwa
Glocke	toke	dawuro
Doppelglocke	gankogui	nnawuta

Alle obengenannten Instrumente können zusammen in einem Ensemble zur Liedbegleitung gespielt werden. Das wichtigste Schlaginstrument ist jedoch die Trommel, die oft auch in Verbindung mit Glocken, Rasseln und Kastagnetten verwendet wird. Selten spielt man nur eine Trommel — meist zwei oder drei verschiedene. In manchen sozialen Gruppen und am Königshof gibt es noch größere Ensembles.

Es gibt verschiedene Arten von Trommeln: Trommeln und Tamburine mit viereckigem Rahmen verschiedener Größen, kleine und große zylindrische, Trommeln in Form eines Fasses, einer Flasche oder einer Sanduhr. Einige davon sind Handtrommeln, die mit Handfläche und Fingern geschlagen werden, andere wieder spielt man mit zwei Schlägeln oder mit der linken Hand und einem Schlägel in der Rechten.

Folgende Trommeln werden hier als Begleitinstrumente genannt:

Ewe: Kaganu	Kleine, hohe Trommel
Asiwui	mittelgroße Trommel, Altlage
Sogo	große Trommel, Tenorlage
Twi: Donno	Trommel in Form einer Sanduhr, gebräuchlich in ganz Ghana
Petia	hohe Trommel
Apentemma	kleine Handtrommel
Atumpan	sprechende Trommeln oder Sprechtrommeln (ein Paar)
Tamale	Trommel oder Tamburin mit viereckigem Rahmen

DAS TROMMELSPIEL

Alle Ghanesen trommeln gern. Deshalb können sie auch mit Trommeln allein oder mit Trommeln in Verbindung mit anderen Schlaginstrumenten — wie zum Beispiel Glocken oder Rasseln — Musik machen. Auch einige einfache Beispiele dieser Art sind hier aufgeführt.

Es ist wohl nicht nötig, auf den Charakter der Musikstücke näher einzugehen; denn ich bin sicher, daß die Musik für sich selbst sprechen wird. Man muß nur immer bedenken, daß der Geist, aus dem Musik in Afrika entsteht, von größter Bedeutung ist; denn für die Menschen in Afrika ist Musik nicht nur eine „schöne Sache", sondern eine mögliche Ausdrucksform lebendiger Gemeinschaftserfahrung.

J. H. Kwabena Nketia

INTRODUCTION

If you visit a town in Ghana on a day on which a public ceremony is being performed or the occasion of an annual harvest festival, you will find that drumming, singing and dancing feature very prominently in the activities of the occasion. Ghanaians, like other African peoples, enjoy making music. Everybody is, therefore, encouraged to learn to sing and dance, so that he can share the joy of music making with others.

There is a large repertoire of musical items that are passed on from generation to generation, but the musical tradition is kept alive not only by this but also by the encouragement that is given to creativity and improvisation during performances.

friends. In Ghana, it is customary to pour libation when one addresses one's ancestors or prays to God, the Supreme Being, or to some lesser deity. One libation song has been included in this selection.

Not all verse is sung. Some are spoken, others are played on instruments, such as *atumpan* talking drums, for drums can be used as substitutes for the speaking voice. (What the drummer does is to imitate the intonation and the rhythm of the speech text on his instrument.) One arrangement of spoken verse (based on texts played on drums) has been included in this selection.

You will have a lot of fun as you try to sing in the three Ghanaian languages represented in this book — in Twi, Ga, and Ewe. All of them sound exactly as written because they are written in some kind of 'phonetic' script. However, a short pronunciation guide has been supplied.

THE SONGS

The songs in this volume have been selected from those performed by the Akan, Ga and Ewe speaking peoples of Ghana. Like other African peoples, Ghanaians have songs for little children, songs for the youth and songs for adults. There are songs sung by various social groups such as religious groups and warriors. There are occasions on which members of these different groups mix. Although little children, for example, perform on their own, they are allowed to join some of the adult groups during story-telling sessions and other social occasions. Hence they learn to sing not only songs belonging to their own age group but also some of those sung by their parents.

The selection in this volume includes cradle songs, songs used for comforting little ones, songs of encouragement and advice, songs about adventurous people and absent

PERCUSSION

The songs in this volume are in strict rhythm and are accompanied by percussion which helps the singer to maintain a steady beat. The simplest and most common form of percussion accompaniment is handclapping. If you are not accustomed to this, you will get a lot of practice as you sing the songs. You should let yourself go whenever you clap. Swing your arms and let your body sway gently as you do this.

There are other percussive instruments that are used for marking equal time divisions or for playing accompanying rhythms. Instead of clapping the hands, two pieces of stick may be struck together. A metal castanet may be used for the same purpose. Another favourite instrument is the single or double clapperless bell or a gong. Then there is the rattle, a very common instrument in Ghana.

Here are some local Ghanaian names for these instruments:

The drums used for accompanying the songs in this volume are as follows:

Instrument	Ewe	Twi
rattle	akaye, axatse	torowa
castanet		firikyiwa
single bell	toke	dawuro
double bell	gankogui	nnawuta

Ewe:	Kaganu:	a small high pitched drum
	Asiwui:	alto drum
	Sogo:	a tenor drum often used as a master drum
Twi:	Donno:	hourglass drum, found all over Ghana
	Petia:	a high pitched drum
	Apentemma:	small hand drum
	Atumpan:	talking drum. It consists of a pair of drums
	Tamale:	square frame drum or tambourine

All the above instruments can be played together in an ensemble for accompanying songs. The most important percussive instrument, however, is the drum. Very often, it is combined with bells, castanets and rattles. A single drum may be used, but it is more common to use two or three different drums. Larger ensembles are used by some social groups and the royal court.

There are different kinds of drums. These are square frame drums or tambourines of different sizes, small and large cylindrical, barrel, bottle shaped or hourglass shaped drums. Some of these are hand drums played with the palm and the fingers. Others are played with two sticks or with the left hand and a stick held in the right hand.

DRUMMING

All Ghanaians enjoy drumming, so they can make music with drums alone, or drums combined with other percussion such as bells and rattles. You will find a couple of simple examples of this kind of music in this volume.

There is no need to comment on the character of the music presented here, for I am sure that the music will speak for itself. Always remember that the spirit in which African music is performed is of paramount importance, because for people in Africa, music is not just a thing of 'beauty' but a mode of expression regarded as a vital part of community experience.

J. H. Kwabena Nketia

HINWEISE FÜR DIE AUSSPRACHE

Vokale:

ɔ : offener, kurzer Laut — nicht wie „o" in „Motte", sondern beinahe wie „a" in „Matte"

ɛ : halboffenes, kurzes „e" — ähnlich wie in „Bett"

e : wird auf zweierlei Arten ausgesprochen — entweder wie „i" in *mit* — oder etwa „ei", also beinahe ein Diphthong wie engl. *„day"*

o : wird auf zweierlei Arten ausgesprochen — entweder offener Vokal wie in „oft" — oder geschlossener Vokal wie in *„Bucht"*

Konsonanten:

ŋ : nasal wie ng in *„singen"*

ḍ : wie „d", doch schlägt die Zunge weiter hinten am Gaumen an

f : wie „f" — mit beiden Lippen ausgesprochen

v : wie „v" — mit beiden Lippen ausgesprochen

x : wie stimmloses „h"

Die folgenden Konsonanten sind Symbolpaare — d. h. jedes Paar steht für nur einen Laut:

dw : wie „g" in *„Gin"* mit Lippenrundung

tw : wie tsch in *„deutsch"* — mit Lippenrundung

hw : flüchtiges „w" — aus der Mundstellung für „u" gebildet

nw : wie „nj" in *„Sonja"* — mit Lippenrundung

gy : wie „g" in *„Gin"*

dz : wie „g" in *„Gin"*

ky : wie „tsch" in *„deutsch"*

hy : wie „sch"

ʃ : wie „sch"

ny : wie „nj" in *„Sonja"*

gb : wie „g" plus „b", gewissermaßen gleichzeitig ausgesprochen

kp : wie „k" und „p" gewissermaßen gleichzeitig ausgesprochen

PRONUNCIATION GUIDE

Vowel sounds:

ɔ : the sound of this letter (written like a reversed c) is like the sound in *cost, hot*

ɛ : the sound of this letter (written like a reversed 3) is close to the sound in *red, pet*

e : is pronounced in two ways:
(a) like i in *sit*, or (b) the beginning of the sound in *hate.*

o : is pronounced in two ways:
(a) as open vowel (like the beginning of the sound in *coat*)

(b) as a close vowel rather like the sound in *put*

Consonants:

ŋ : velar nasal like ng in *sing*

ɖ : like d pronounced slighly further back

f : like f pronounced with both lips

v : like v pronounced with both lips

x : like h without voice.

The following consonants are digraphs, that is each pair represents one sound

dw : like j in *Jack* but pronounced with lip rounding

tw : like ch in *chair* but pronounced with lip rounding

hw : like wh in *where*, but may also be fronted

nw : like ny in *Bunyan*, but pronounced with lip rounding

gy : like j in *Jack*

(dz(a) : like j in Jack

ky : like ch in *chair*

hy : like sh in *shop*

ʃ : like sh in *shop*

ny : like ny in *Bunyan*

gb : like g pronounced simultaneously with b

kp : like k pronounced simultaneously with p

INSTRUMENTS

Handclapping

Rattle (axatse)

Rattle (Akaye)

Castanets

Bell (Dawuro)

Double Bell (Gakogui)

Double Gong (nnawuta)

Hand-Drum

Hand Drum (Apantemma)

Small Hig-Pitched Drum (Kaganu)

Small High-Pitched Drum (Petia)

Hand-Drum (Asiwui)

Large Drum (Sogo)

Hourglass Drum (Dondo)

Small Frame-Drum

Small High-Pitched Frame-Drum

Medium Low-Pitched Frame-Drum

Adowa Drum Ensemble

Atumpan (talking Drums)   Petia (high pitched Drum)   Apentemma (hand Drum)

Donno (hourglass Drums)   Dawuro (single Bell)

Agbadza Drum Ensemble

Kaganu   Gankogui   Asiwui

      Axatse   Sogo

Adowa Drum Ensemble

Atumpan
(talking Drums resting on stand)

Donno
(hourglass Drums
in Foreground)

Petia
(high pitched Drum)
Dawuro
(resting against Petia)

Apentemma
(Hand Drum)

Dawuro (single Bell)   Axatse (Rattle)   Gankogui (double Bell)

Nnawuta

INDEX

An Ewe Cradle Song with rhythmic accompaniment

Tu! Tu! Gbɔvi

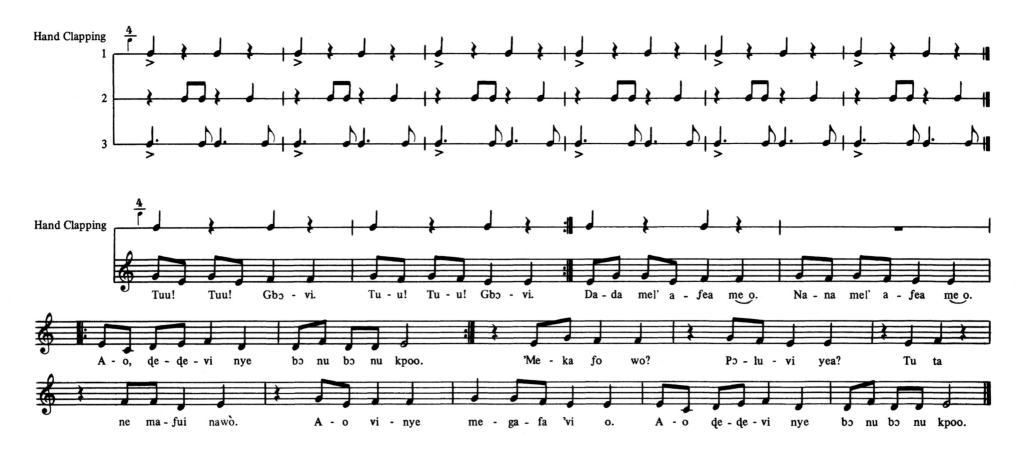

Tuu! Tuu! Gbɔvi,
Tuu! Tuu! Gbɔvi.
Dada me l'a fea me o.
Nana me l'a fea me o.
Ao, dedevi nye, bɔnu, bɔnu kpoo.
'Meka fo wò?
Pɔluvi yea?
Tu ta, ne mafui nawò.
Ao, vinye, megafa 'vi o.
Ao, dedevi nye bɔnu, bɔnu kpoo.

Away, away, little goat,
Away, away, little goat.
mamma is not at home.
Grandmama is not at home.
Oh, my little child, keep quiet.
Who spanked you?
Is it little Paul?
Spit and let me spank him for you,
Oh, my child, don't cry.
Oh, my poor child keep quiet.

Miwɔe Nenyo

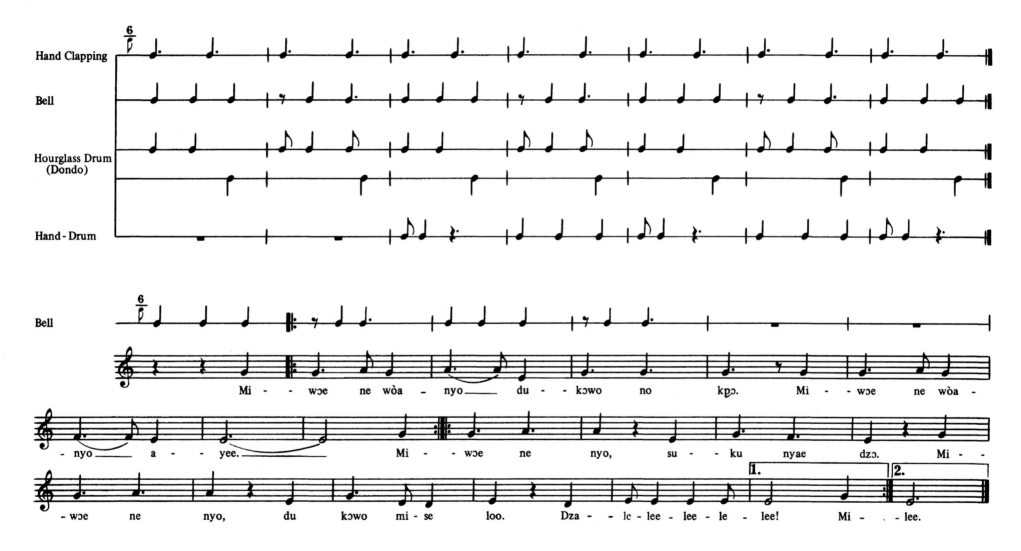

Miwɔe ne woa nyo, dukɔwo no kpɔ.	You must do it well for others to see.
Miwɔe ne woa nyo, ayee.	You must do it well.
Miwɔe ne nyo, suku nyae dzɔ	You must do it well, it's an era of education.
Miwɔe ne nyo, dukɔwo mise loo.	You must do it well for others to see.
Dza le lee leele lee!	Dzaleleeleelee! (An exclamation).

A Ga Tune with rhythmic accompaniment

Kelo aba wɔye

Solo: Kɛ lo aba wɔye   Bring us fish to eat
           Kɛ lo aba wɔye, Tɔtɔle   Bring us fish to eat, 'Tɔtɔle'
Chorus: Kɛ lo aba wɔye, kɛ lo aba wɔye.   Bring us fish to eat.

An Ewe Tune with rhythmic accompaniment

Klinua Miedo Do vɔ

Solo: Klinua miedo ɖo vɔ.
Chorus: Aɖatsia ge.
Solo: Miatɔ gbadzaviawo, klinuanu miedo ɖo vɔ.
Chorus: Aɖatsia ge, dzimelefowo na gbugbɔ.

We've arrived at Klinua.
The tears drop
Fettow "gbadza" players, we've arrived at 'Klinua'.
The tears drop, if you are not brave, return.

An Ewe Lament with rhythmic accompaniment

Dzi tɔ de l'agbe nam

Solo: Dzitɔ ɖe l'a-gbe nam
Ne agbenya mahiam o.
Ne nyewo dzitɔ ɖe l'agbe,
Ne agbenya mahiam o.
Ne nyewo dzitɔ ɖe l'agbe
Ne agbenya mahiam o, loo.
Amegba viwo zu Ganahɛ yi afume ɖo fe.
Nyitse ma kpɔ Ganahɛ wo afume ɖo fe ɖa.

Chorus: Yee, Ganahɛ yi afume ɖo fe.
Nyitse makpɔ Ganahɛ wo afume ɖo fe ɖa.

If I had a brave man alive,
I would not be bothered by problems of life.
If I had a brave man alive,
I would not be bothered by problems of life.
If a brave man of my own were alive,
I would not be bothered by problems of life.
Children of the best ones are about to drown in the sea like a pig.
I must also witness the drowning of the pig.

The pig is about to get drowned.
I must also witness the drowning of the pig.

Song with rhythmic accompaniment

Taa, Taa, yee

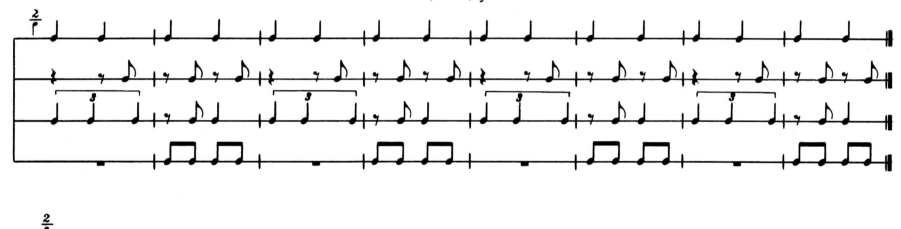

Taa, taa, tee,
yee, yee, yee,
Kaafo ama.
Yaa, ya A-wusi o.

Taa, taa, tee.
Yee, yee, yee.
Don't cry.
Yaa, ya—Awusi o.

Speech Choir with drum accompaniment (Akan)

Mede brebre masi ta

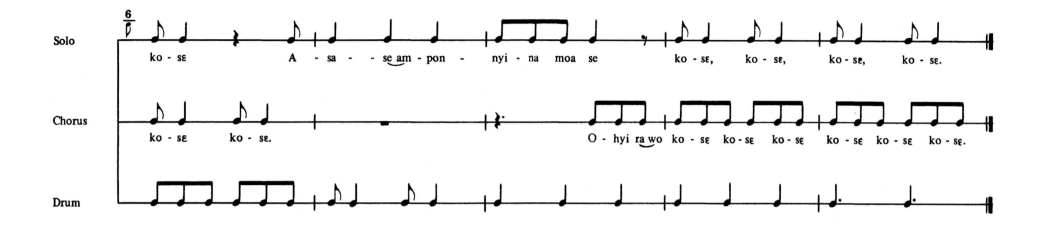

Mede brɛbrɛ, masi ta.	I go slowly, I walk slowly.
Afe ano ahyia,	The year has come.
Merebɛma wo adwo	I come to greet you.
Nyini, nyini, nyini,	grow, grow, grow,
Nyini bɔ akora.	grow to an old age.
Otweaduampɔn Nyame se,	God Almighty sends you
Ohyira wo kosɛ, kosɛ, kosɛ.	Blessings, Blessings, Blessings.
Asase amponnyinamoa se	Mother Earth greets you
Ohyira wo kosɛ, kosɛ, kosɛ.	And blesses you, blesses you.

This piece is a simplified version of the Ewe Anlo Agbadza.
All parts except the Large Drum repeat given rhythm patterns

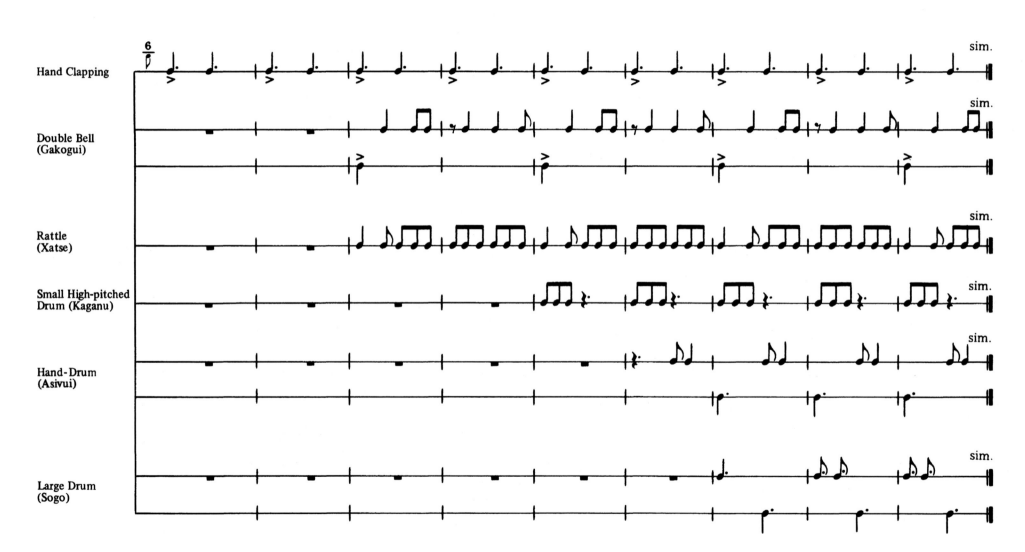

Hand Clapping

Double Bell
(Gakogui)

Rattle
(Xatse)

Small High-pitched
Drum (Kaganu)

Hand-Drum
(Asivui)

Large Drum
(Sogo)

Kondo yi Yevuwo de megbɔ o

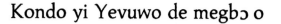

Double Bell

Solo — Kon - do yi ye - vuwo de, me - gbɔ o. Da - da be mi - va mi - tso gbe ɖe 'dzi. Kon - do yi

ye - vuwo de, me - gbɔ o _____ mi - tso gbe ɖe 'dzi. Kon - do yi Ye - vuwo de, me - gbɔ o, Da - da be

mi - va mi - tso gbe ɖe 'dzi. Kon - do yi ye - vuwo de, me - gbɔ o. _____ Mi - tso gbe ɖe 'dzi.

Solo: Kondo yi Yevuwo de, megbɔ o,
           Dada be miva mítso gbe ɖe 'dzi.

Chorus: Kondo yi Yevuwo de, megbɔ o,
           Mitso gbe ɖe 'dzi.

Kondo went to the whiteman's world and never returned.
Let us bet, said the mother.

Kondo went to the whiteman's world and never returned.
Let us bet.

This piece is based on the Ghanaian Highlife "Osibi" (simplified).
All parts except the Hand-Drum repeat given rhythm patterns

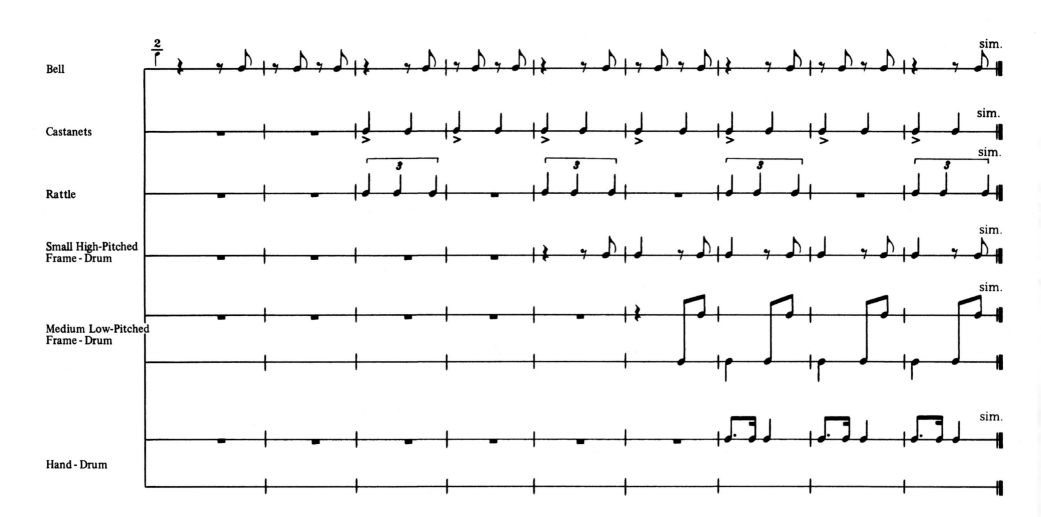

Samanfo, begye nsa nom

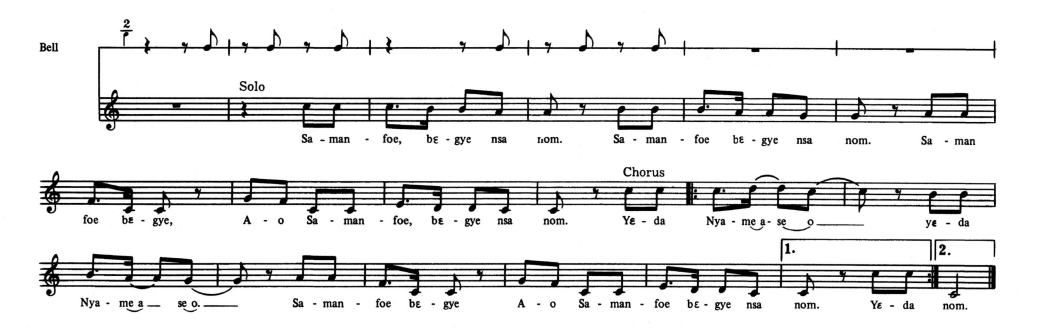

Solo;   Samanfo e, bɛgye nsa nom.
Samanfo e, bɛgye nsa nom.
Samanfo e, bɛgye,
Ao, Samanfo e, bɛgye nsa nom.

Chorus: ‖: Yɛda Nyame ase o :‖
Samanfo e, bɛgye nsa nom
Ao, Samanfo e, bɛgye nsa nom.

Departed Spirits, come for a drink.
Departed Spirits, come for a drink.
Departed Spirits, come and receive,
Ao, departed Spirits, come for a drink.

We thank God.
Departed Spirits, come and receive,
Ao, Departed Spirits, come for a drink.

Drum Ensemble based on Akan "Asaadua" (simplified).

All parts except the large Frame-Drum repeat given rhythm patterns.

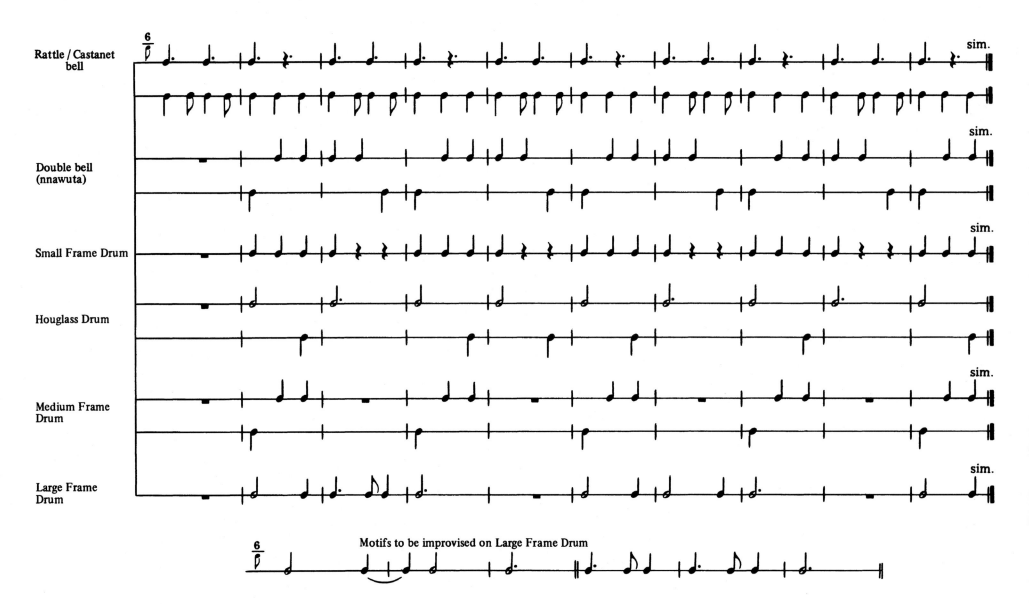

Motifs to be improvised on Large Frame Drum

Mesu mefre agya, Katakyie

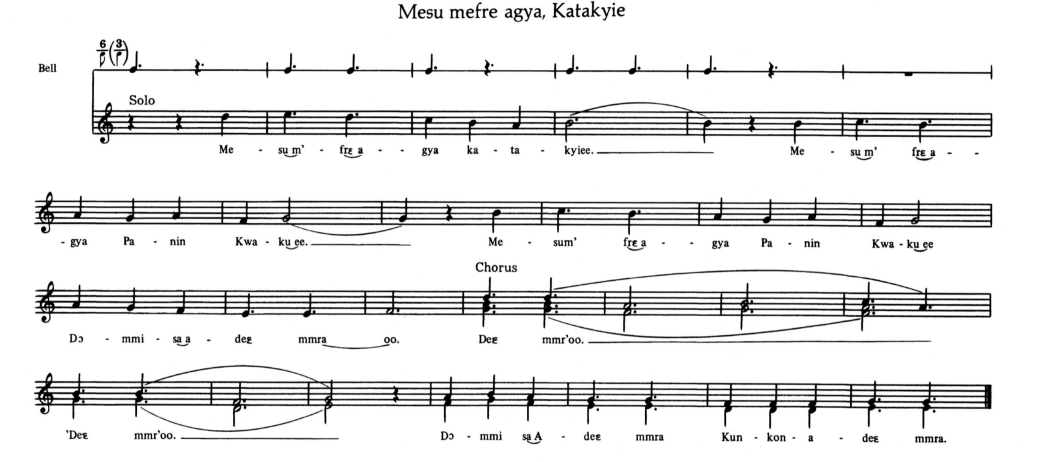

Solo: Mesu mefrɛ agya, katakyie.
mesu mefrɛ agya, Panin Kwaku.
Mesu mefrɛ agya, Panin Kwaku
Dɔmmisa, adeɛ mmra o.

Chorus: Adeɛ mmra o.
Dɔmmisa, adeɛ mmra.
Kunkon, adeɛ mmra.

I cry out for the valiant one.
Opanin Kwaku, our leader.
I cry out for valiant Kwaku
Leader of the host, precious one, come to us.

Come to us, precious one.
Come to us leader of the host.
Come to us, great one.

Ensemblef or non-melodic instruments based on Akan "Adowa" (simplified).
All parts except "Atumpan" repeat given rhythm patterns till the end of piece.
The "Atumpan" may improvise on motifs of given patterns.

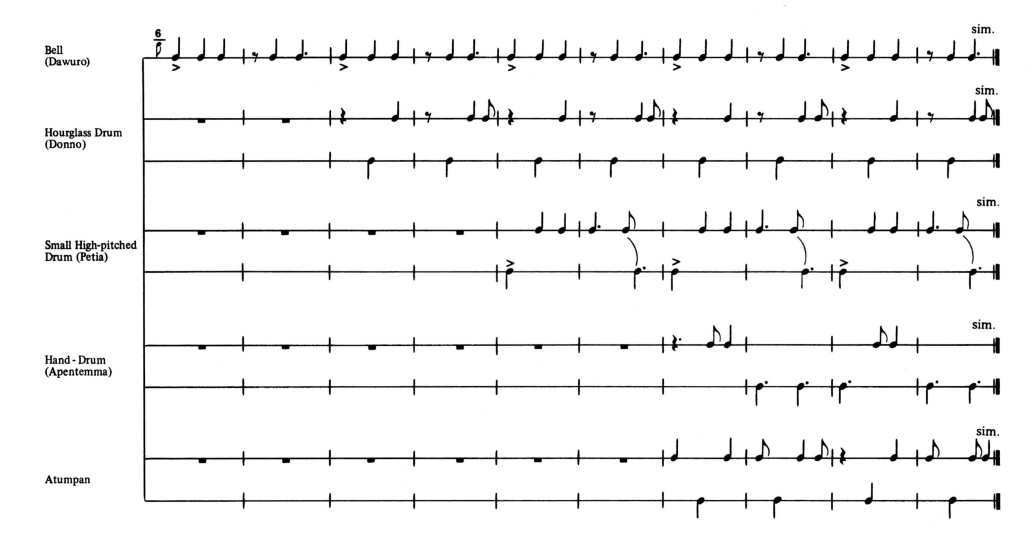

Adu e bɔ yen dwa oo (Adowa)

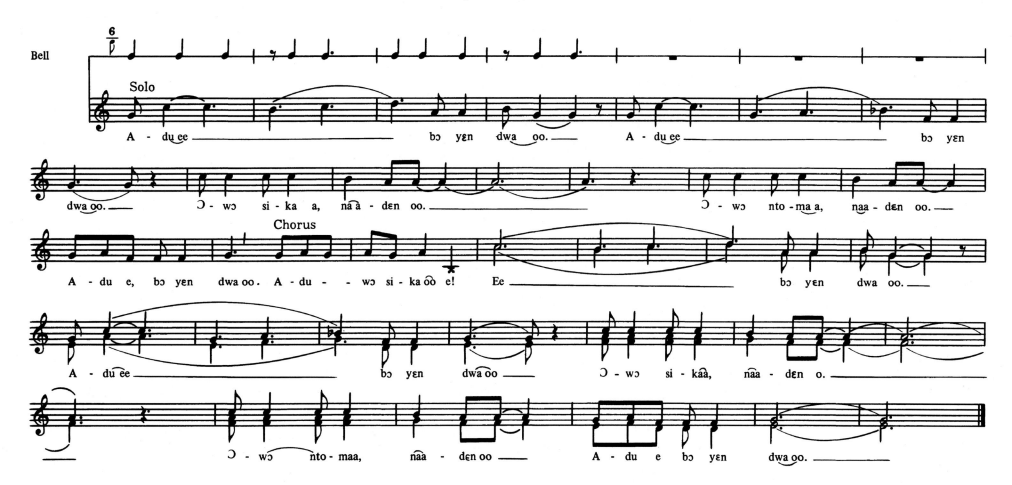

Solo: Adu e, bɔ yɛn dwa oo.	Adu, get ready to receive us.
Adu e, bɔ yɛn dwa oo.	Adu, get ready to receive us.
Ɔwɔ sika a, na adɛn oo?	What does it matter if he has money?
Ɔwɔ ntoma a, na adɛn oo?	What does it matter if he has cloth?
Chorus: Adu e, bɔ yɛn dwa oo.	Adu, get ready to receive us.
Adu ɔwɔ sika oo-e,	Adu, the rich man,
Ee bɔ yɛn dwa oo.	Get ready to receive us.
Adu e, bɔ yɛn dwa oo?	Adu, get ready to receive us.
Ɔwɔ sika a na adɛn oo?	What does it matter if he has money?
Ɔwɔ ntoma a, na adɛn oo?	What does it matter if he has cloth?
Adu e, bɔ yɛn dwa oo.	Adu, get ready to receive us.

A Ga Cradle Song with rhythmic accompaniment

Kaa Fo

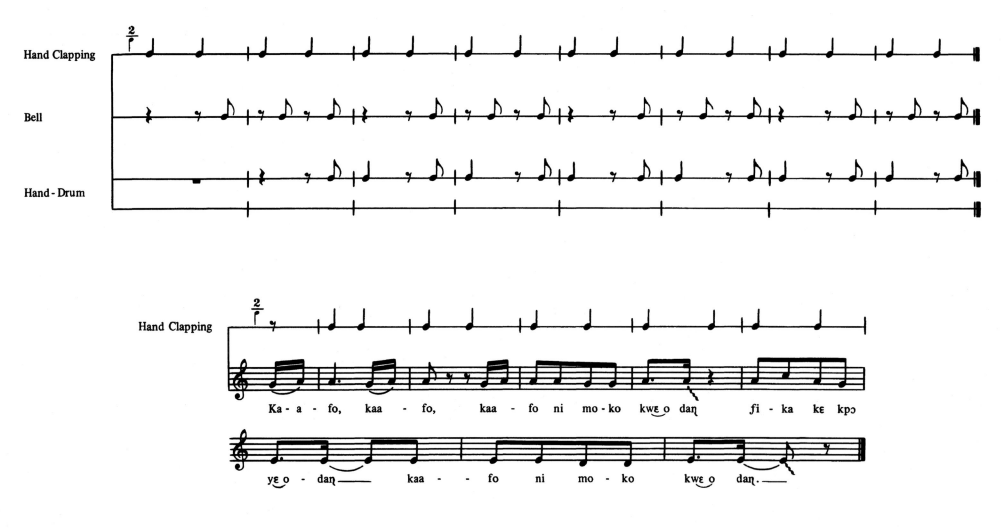

Ka - a - fo, kaa - fo, kaa - fo ni mo - ko kwε o daŋ ʃi - ka kε kpɔ

yε o - daŋ kaa - fo ni mo - ko kwε o daŋ.

Kaafo, kaafo,
Kaafo ni moko kwε odaŋ
ʃika kε kpɔ yε odaɔ
Kaafo ni moko kwε odaŋ.

Don't cry, don't cry,
Don't cry and let anyone see your mouth
There is gold in your mouth
Don't cry and let anyone see your mouth.

Schott Music, Mainz 42 998